Contents

MINI-PROJECT

Answers to the questions are on the back of the Pull-out Poster in the centre of the book.

This book covers unit 5B from the year five scheme of work

Published by Coordination Group Publications Ltd.

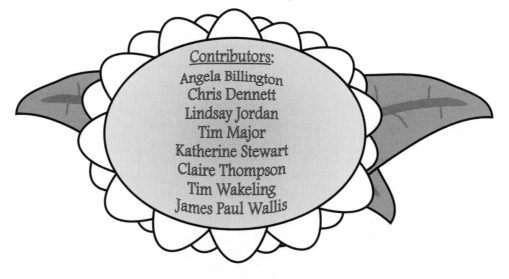

Contributors:
Angela Billington
Chris Dennett
Lindsay Jordan
Tim Major
Katherine Stewart
Claire Thompson
Tim Wakeling
James Paul Wallis

ISBN: 978 1 84146 267 7
Groovy website: www.cgpbooks.co.uk
Jolly bits of clipart from CorelDRAW®
Printed by Elanders Ltd, Newcastle upon Tyne.

Based on the classic CGP style created by Richard Parsons.

Flowering Plants

Plants don't just have flowers to <u>look nice</u>, they're there for a special job. Flowers have <u>seeds</u> inside them. Sometimes flowers turn into <u>fruit</u> and sometimes they dry up and leave the seeds.

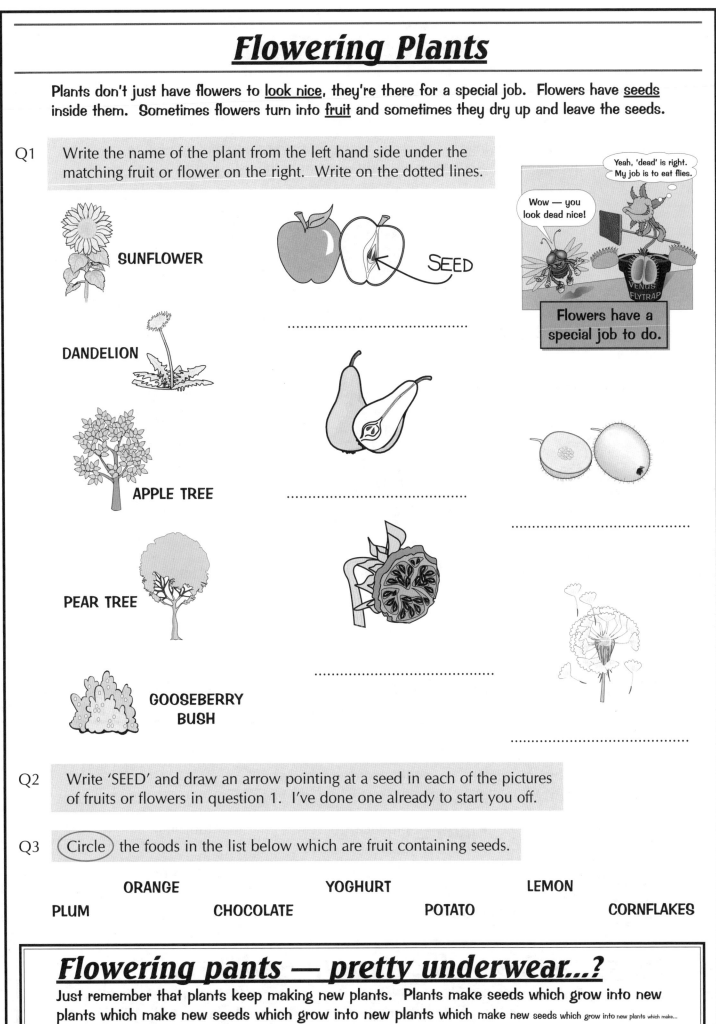

Q1 Write the name of the plant from the left hand side under the matching fruit or flower on the right. Write on the dotted lines.

SUNFLOWER

DANDELION

APPLE TREE

PEAR TREE

GOOSEBERRY BUSH

SEED

Wow — you look dead nice!

Yeah, 'dead' is right. My job is to eat flies.

VENUS FLYTRAP

Flowers have a special job to do.

....

....

....

....

....

Q2 Write 'SEED' and draw an arrow pointing at a seed in each of the pictures of fruits or flowers in question 1. I've done one already to start you off.

Q3 Circle the foods in the list below which are fruit containing seeds.

ORANGE   YOGHURT   LEMON

PLUM   CHOCOLATE   POTATO   CORNFLAKES

Flowering pants — pretty underwear...?

Just remember that plants keep making new plants. Plants make seeds which grow into new plants which make new seeds which <u>grow</u> into new plants which make new seeds which grow into new plants which make...

Flowering Plants

This page is all about what comes when. First comes the <u>seed</u> and then the <u>plant</u>.
After that come <u>flowers</u> then seeds again (or for some plants <u>fruit</u> and then seeds).

Q1 Look at this picture showing how the seed of the fruit grows into a plant. Fill in
the gap in the sentence below using the right word from the list on the bucket.

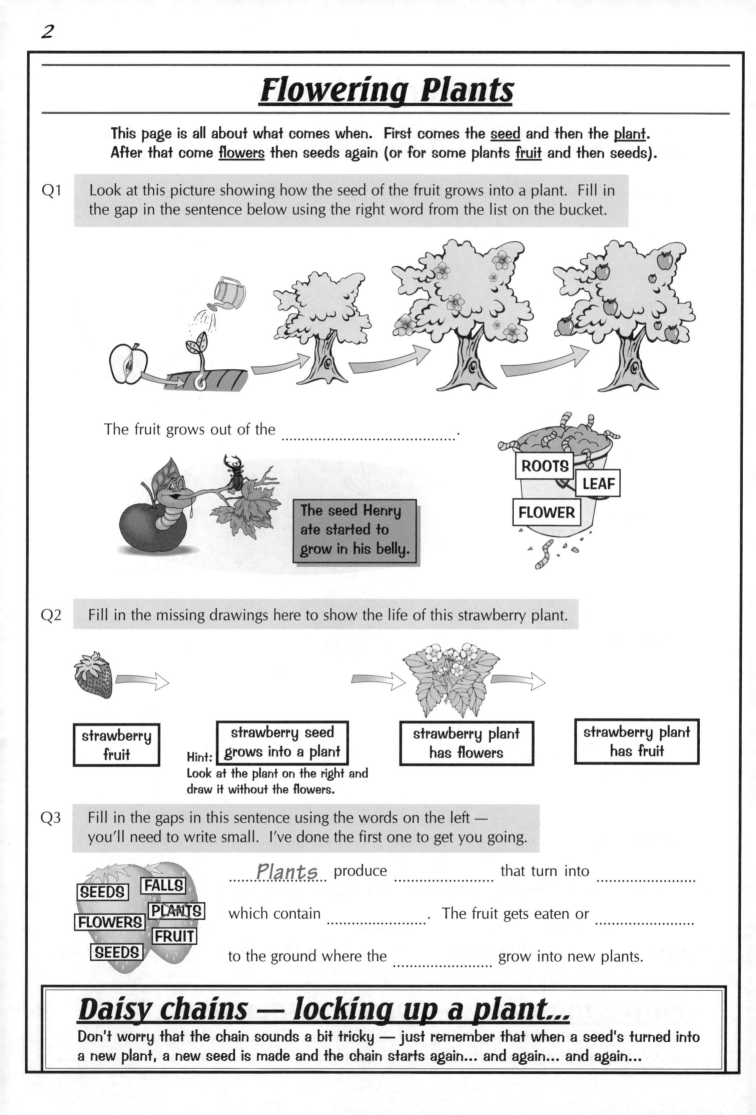

The fruit grows out of the ....

The seed Henry ate started to grow in his belly.

ROOTS
LEAF
FLOWER

Q2 Fill in the missing drawings here to show the life of this strawberry plant.

| strawberry fruit | Hint: strawberry seed grows into a plant | strawberry plant has flowers | strawberry plant has fruit |

Hint: Look at the plant on the right and draw it without the flowers.

Q3 Fill in the gaps in this sentence using the words on the left —
you'll need to write small. I've done the first one to get you going.

SEEDS FALLS
PLANTS
FLOWERS
FRUIT
SEEDS

.....Plants..... produce .... that turn into ....

which contain .... The fruit gets eaten or ....

to the ground where the .... grow into new plants.

Daisy chains — locking up a plant...

Don't worry that the chain sounds a bit tricky — just remember that when a seed's turned into
a new plant, a new seed is made and the chain starts again... and again... and again...

Flowering Plants

Plants get old and die just like people do — but people have <u>babies</u> and plants have <u>seeds</u>.
Seeds are <u>important</u> because when they grow they turn into <u>new plants</u>.

Q1 Fill in the gaps in these sentences using one of the choices from the brackets.

Fruits and seeds are .... (IMPORTANT / NOT IMPORTANT) because they fall

to the ground and .... (GROW INTO / FEED) new baby plants. Without

them there would be .... (NO NEW / SMALLER) flowering plants.

When you grow up you'll be a great big tree just like your father and me, Pip.

But I want to be a hairdresser...!

Little seeds grow into big trees.

Q2 Look at the sentence about flowering plants below — draw a line joining it to the sentence on the right that means the same thing.

Flowering plants reproduce.

(A) Plants with flowers make seeds which grow into new baby plants.

(B) Plants with flowers die in the winter.

(C) Plants grow flowers which turn into baby plants and then fall off.

Q3 Here are a whole load of sentences about fruits and seeds — some are true and some are false. Put a 'T' in the box next to the true ones and an 'F' next to the false ones.

(1) All plants grow fruit.

(2) New plants explode out of the middle of flowers.

(3) Flowering plants produce seeds from their flowers.

(4) Fruit grows on the plant where the flowers were, as soon as the flowers fall off.

Flower power — they just keep on growing...

All living things need to reproduce — or they would die out. Seeds are a bit like a baby before it's born — they're the plant's way of making sure there are more plants. That's pretty important.

Seed Dispersal

Plants spread their seeds so that more plants of the <u>same</u> type will grow in <u>new</u> areas, and all the new plants won't try and grow in the same place. This gives the new plants more room and a better chance of surviving. This is called 'seed dispersal'.

Q1 Some plants use the wind to spread their seeds. Other plants use animals by wrapping their seeds in fruit — the animal eats the fruit, and when it goes to the toilet the seed pops out along with the other waste. Look at the pictures then write the sentences from the blob in the right place in the table.

Seeds from the peach tree are dispersed by animals. This is an <u>animal dispersed</u> seed.

Seeds from the dandelion are dispersed by the wind. This is a <u>wind dispersed</u> seed.

They are too heavy to float on the wind.   They are very light.   They float easily on the wind.
They are surrounded by tasty fruit.   They are not nice to eat.   They are often brightly coloured.

THINGS ABOUT ANIMAL DISPERSED SEEDS	THINGS ABOUT WIND DISPERSED SEEDS

Q2 Write 'A' next to the seeds below which are dispersed by animals, and 'W' next to those which are dispersed by wind. Write the letter in the box.

Cherry   Sycamore   Plum   Thistle

Q3 Most seeds are dispersed by animals or wind, but some use other methods. Use the words from the brackets to fill in the gaps in these sentences about the dispersal of coconuts.

A coconut is too .... (hard / big) to be eaten and too

.... (heavy / high up) to be carried by the wind.

Because of this coconuts must be dispersed by

.... (seagulls / water).

One kind of crab does actually eat coconuts. Coconut crabs climb up the tree and pull off the coconuts so that they fall and smash on the ground. Then the crabs scurry down and eat them.

Which purse? — dispersal be fine...

You don't have to <u>remember</u> how each different seed is dispersed. Just think: if it's <u>light</u>, the <u>wind</u> will blow it away. If it's <u>bright</u> and looks <u>tasty</u>, chances are some animal will come along and eat it.

Seed Dispersal

You can guess how a plant spreads its seeds by looking at the seed's <u>shape</u>, <u>size</u> and <u>weight</u> and whether it's got <u>fruit</u> or not. You need to use your brain a bit — and follow the clues.

Q1   Have a good look at these two seeds and think about what the information tells you. Write underneath each of them <u>how</u> you think they would be dispersed. On the lines underneath that, write <u>why</u> you think it would be dispersed that way.

This seed is light and propeller shaped. It is about as long as your middle finger.

These seeds are in a group inside a fleshy fruit. The fruit is fairly heavy and is about the size of your fist.

Cripes — I'm gonna have to lose a lot of weight if I want to float off in the wind.

<u>Dispersed by:</u> ....

<u>Why:</u> ....

<u>Dispersed by:</u> ....

<u>Why:</u> ....

Heavy fruits don't float on the wind.

Q2   Another way some plants disperse their seeds is actually <u>exploding</u> them out — like a kind of little natural bomb. Put a tick in the box next to the right reason why plants explode their seeds out and don't just let them fall to the ground.

Broom is a common moorland plant with yellow flowers. Its seeds grow inside pods shaped like pea or bean pods. When the pods dry out the two sides twist around until they split suddenly, exploding the seeds out.

Plants explode their seeds out:

☐ — so that they scare off animals.

☐ — to look good and attract attention.

☐ — to spread their seeds over a wider area.

Broom seed pods

Seed

Broom in flower

Q3   Name four different types of seed dispersal. I've done one for you. Write on the lines.

① *animal*

② ....

③ ....

④ ....

Seed

There is another type of animal dispersal too. Some plants have sticky seeds which attach themselves to animals and get carried off.

Dog

<u>Animal dispersal — like when it rains cats and dogs...</u>

Plants are ace. They've got all these groovy ways to make sure their <u>seeds get planted</u> all round the countryside. Then we get to watch loads more little plants growing where they landed. Cool.

6

MINI-PROJECT
Germination of Seeds — Warmth

I want to know what makes seeds start to grow (germinate). To start with, here's an experiment to see if the <u>temperature</u> affects whether seeds germinate.

I have put pots with seeds into 3 glass boxes, which are at <u>different temperatures</u>.

How The Seeds Were Planted

Seed — the same type of seed in each pot, buried in the same way.

Soil — the same amount of soil in each pot.

Water — each pot stands in the same amount of water.

10 pots were kept at 2 °C

10 pots were kept at 25 °C

10 pots were kept at 65 °C

To make it a fair test, they were all the <u>same type</u> of seeds, got the <u>same amount</u> of sunlight, water and soil, and were all <u>buried</u> in the <u>same way</u>. Only the temperature was different in each box.

Q1 For it to be a fair test on whether temperature affects how seeds grow, why is it important that they are all the same types of seeds? Tick one answer.

☐ So that the plants look pretty when they grow.

☐ If people want to take the plants home at the end of the experiment, everyone will get the same type of plant.

☐ Seeds from some plants germinate more quickly than seeds from other plants, so if you use seeds from different plants you won't know if the time the seeds take to germinate is because of the temperature or not.

You only need a small hole to bury a seed.

Q2 For it to be a fair test, why is it important that all the seeds have the same amount of sunlight? (Write one reason.)

....

....

Q3 For it to be a fair test, why is it important that all the seeds were buried in the same way? (Write one reason.)

....

....

Why are thermometers cross? — TEMPER-ature...

It's really important to make this experiment a <u>fair test</u> if you want to find out if temperature definitely affects seed germination. Remember a fair test is one where <u>only one thing</u> changes.

Germination of Seeds— Warmth

MINI-PROJECT

I did the experiment from the last page by checking the pots at 9 o'clock every other morning. I knew that a seed had germinated if a seedling could be seen pushing through the soil.

Q1　I did the experiment and wrote a diary of the results in my notepad. Fill in the table on the right, with the numbers of seeds that had germinated in each of the boxes on each day.

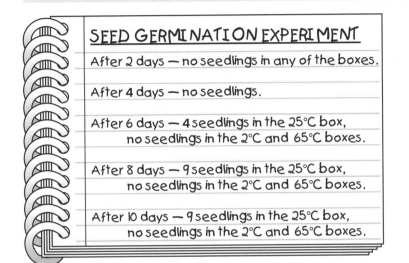

SEED GERMINATION EXPERIMENT

After 2 days — no seedlings in any of the boxes.

After 4 days — no seedlings.

After 6 days — 4 seedlings in the 25°C box, no seedlings in the 2°C and 65°C boxes.

After 8 days — 9 seedlings in the 25°C box, no seedlings in the 2°C and 65°C boxes.

After 10 days — 9 seedlings in the 25°C box, no seedlings in the 2°C and 65°C boxes.

	2°C	25°C	65°C
2 days			
4 days			
6 days			
8 days			
10 days			

Q2　This is my conclusion about the results. Draw a (ring) round the word in the brackets that makes the sentence correct.

Temperature [DOES / DOESN'T] affect whether or not a seed germinates.

Q3　Out of the temperatures tested, which did the seeds germinate best in? Tick the right box.

☐ 2°C　　☐ 25°C　　☐ 65°C

Plants can be dangerous.

Q4　Why do you think only 9 seeds germinated out of the 10 seeds in the 25°C box? Choose the right answer, and write it out.

One of the seeds was probably a dead seed.　　*The seed was much colder than the others.*

A mouse came and ate the seed.　　*Some seeds are invisible.*

....

....

Why are seeds unhealthy? — GERM-ination...

There's a fair bit to learn on this page and from this experiment. Temperature is important for the germination of seeds, but <u>not all</u> seeds are alive and can grow — some are just dead as dodos.

8

MINI-PROJECT

Germination of Seeds — Light

I want to know if <u>light</u> affects whether seeds germinate (start to grow). To find out if seeds germinate better in the light or in the dark, I could do an experiment.

Q1 Read these sentences about ways to do this light experiment. Some of them are good ways, and some of them are bad ways. Choose 3 good ways, and write them out below.

Plant some seeds really deep and others really close to the surface.

Put half of the pots with seeds in a dark place, and half in a light place.

Give all seeds the same amount of water.

Put most of the pots with seeds in the dark, and just one pot in the light.

Plant all seeds 1 cm under the soil.

Don't bother watering some of the plants.

....

....

....

....

Q2 I did the experiment and wrote a diary of the results in my notepad. Fill in the table on the right, to say how many seeds had germinated in the dark and how many had germinated in the light after each number of days.

SEED GERMINATION — LIGHT EXPERIMENT

At the start of the experiment 10 pots with seeds were put in the dark, and 10 were put in the light

After 2 days — no seedlings in the dark, no seedlings in the light.

After 4 days — 1 seedling in the dark, no seedlings in the light.

After 6 days — 5 seedlings in the dark, 4 seedlings in the light.

After 8 days — 8 seedlings in the dark, 9 seedlings in the light.

After 10 days — 9 seedlings in the dark, 9 seedlings in the light.

After:	Dark	Light
2 days		
4 days		
6 days		
8 days		
10 days		

Q3 Write 'does' or 'does not' in the gap to complete this conclusion about the results.

Light .... affect whether or not a seed germinates.

Lindsay thought she had to watch the seeds all night.

The Plant Robot — Germinator... I'll be back...

This fair test business means you have to think extra hard about how to carry out the experiment. You have to be <u>dead careful</u> with the method if you want to make sure you get good results.

9

Germination of Seeds — Soil

MINI-PROJECTMINI-PROJECT

To find out whether seeds need <u>soil</u> to germinate, you could do an experiment where some seeds are put in soil, and other seeds are put on a piece of kitchen roll.

Q1 Read these pairs of sentences about ways to do the experiment. Tick the correct sentence from each pair, to show which is the best way of doing the experiment.

☐ Give twice as much water to the seeds in the soil. **OR** Give all the seeds the same amount of water. ☐

☐ Put 10 seeds on kitchen roll, and 10 in soil in a pot. **OR** Put one seed on kitchen roll and 50 in soil. ☐

☐ Check some seeds at 9am every other day and the others at 3pm. **OR** Check all the seeds at 9am every other day. ☐

☐ Make sure all the seeds have the same amount of warmth. **OR** Make sure some of the seeds are loads colder than the other seeds. ☐

Q2 Do the experiment using seeds that will germinate quickly — like radish, cress, lettuce or spring onion seeds. Follow the instructions that you ticked in Q1. Every other day for 14 days, check the number of seeds which have germinated, and write it down in the table below. (If you can't do the experiment, use the spare results from the bottom of the page.)

Hint: Put the seeds on the <u>surface</u> of the soil, so you can see them as soon as they germinate. Normally, you would put them <u>just below</u> the surface, but this time you need to be able to compare them to the seeds on the kitchen roll.

Number of seeds which had germinated, after...						
2 days	4 days	6 days	8 days	10 days	12 days	14 days
In soil						
On kitchen roll						

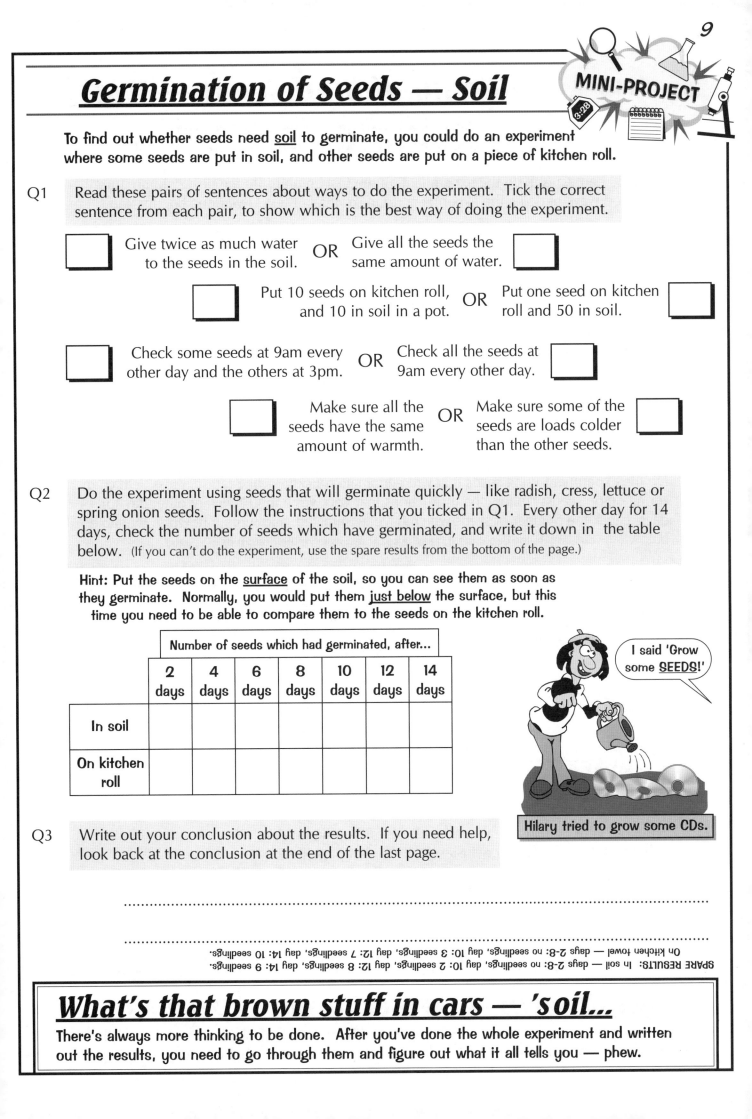

I said 'Grow some <u>SEEDS!</u>'

Hilary tried to grow some CDs.

Q3 Write out your conclusion about the results. If you need help, look back at the conclusion at the end of the last page.

....

....

SPARE RESULTS: In soil — days 2-8: no seedlings, day 10: 2 seedlings, day 12: 8 seedlings, day 14: 9 seedlings.
On kitchen towel — days 2-8: no seedlings, day 10: 3 seedlings, day 12: 7 seedlings, day 14: 10 seedlings.

What's that brown stuff in cars — 'soil...

There's always more thinking to be done. After you've done the whole experiment and written out the results, you need to go through them and figure out what it all tells you — phew.

10

MINI-PROJECT
Germination of Seeds — Water

Seeds might need <u>water</u> in order to germinate.
To be sure whether they do, you need to do an experiment.

Q1 Read the bad ways to do the experiment, in the first column. In the next column, turn them into good ways of doing the experiment, to make it a fair test. I've done one for you.

Bad Way	Good Way
Use seeds from one plant for the seeds with water, and different seeds for the seeds without water.	
Keep the seeds with water cold, and the seeds without water warm.	Keep all the seeds at the same temperature.
Bury the seeds with water deep in the soil, and the seeds without water just under the surface.	

Q2 Do the experiment using seeds that will germinate quickly — like radish, cress, lettuce or spring onion seeds. Follow the instructions that you wrote in Q1. Every other day for 14 days, check the number of seeds which have germinated, and write it down in the table below. (If you can't do the experiment, use the spare results from the bottom of the page.)

Sue made sure her seeds had plenty of water.

	Number of seeds which had germinated, after...						
	2 days	4 days	6 days	8 days	10 days	12 days	14 days
With water							
Without water							

Q3 Write out your conclusion about the results. If you need a bit of help, look back at the conclusion at the end of page 8.

....

....

SPARE RESULTS: **Without water**— days 2-8: no seedlings, day 10: no seedlings, day 12: no seedlings, day 14: no seedlings.
With water — days 2-8: no seedlings, day 10: 2 seedlings, day 12: 8 seedlings, day 14: 9 seedlings.

Growing seeds — 'water' great experiment...

Phew. Every time you want to do a new experiment, you have to think about each one of the things involved. You can't think 'Well, I did that last time so I won't bother today.' No way.

Germination of Seeds

These questions are about all of the experiments on the last 5 pages.

Q1 Fill in this table to show the results from the four experiments about germination of seeds (you should look back at the tables you've already filled in).

	Seeds at 2°C	Seeds at 25°C	Seeds at 65°C	Seeds in dark	Seeds in light	Seeds with soil	Seeds without soil	Seeds with water	Seeds without water
Number of seeds that had germinated at the end of the experiment									

Q2 Fill in the blanks in this conclusion, by choosing from the words below. Use each word only once.

Seeds .... need .... and the right .... to

germinate, but they .... need .... or ....

temperature   soil   do   don't   light   water

These experiments have been about what a seed needs to start growing. For the next questions, think about what the seedling will need to keep growing into a healthy plant as well.

Q3 Pick the right words from the brackets to complete these sentences.

Light .... [DOES / DOES NOT] affect the growth of a plant after germination.

Soil .... [IS / IS NOT] needed by the plant for stability, after germination.

Q4 In your own words, write out what the best conditions are for a seed to germinate and grow into a healthy plant. Include temperature, light, soil and water.

....

....

....

....

....

....

BEFORE   AFTER

Some seeds stay in the ground all winter, and don't grow until it gets warm in the spring. In the desert, seeds can wait in the ground for years until it rains and then they grow very quickly.

Don't hassle plants — leaf them alone...

Plants need loads of things to grow and stay alive. They need everything that the seed needed to start growing. But plants need other things, too — like light. Pretty demanding things, plants.

Insect and Wind Pollination

Pollination is very important for plant reproduction. Pollen is made in one part of the flower but a different part of the flower needs it to make seeds. It is better if a plant is pollinated by pollen from a <u>different plant</u> — but it must be the <u>same type</u> of plant.

Mmm... tasty nectar.

Bee flying in search of nectar to eat.

Pollen from flower's stamen sticks to the bee's back and legs.

The bee flies off in search of more nectar.

When the bee goes to another flower, some of the pollen from the first flower rubs off.

Q1 Look at the pictures of the bee pollinating a plant. Draw lines joining the questions on the left with the right answer on the right.

When I grow up, I want to be a lawyer, like my dad.

When I grow up, I want to be a bee.

Frank was very attracted to flowers.

Why does the bee go to the flower?	Bees carry it.
What part of the flower does the pollen come from?	The stamen.
How does the pollen get carried from one plant to the next?	To eat the nectar.
How do plants attract bees?	It sticks to their backs and legs.
How do the bees carry the pollen?	They have brightly coloured flowers.

Q2 Fill in the blanks in these sentences explaining all the different stages of pollination. Use each of the words below just once.

The plant makes pollen on its .... inside its flowers. It attracts the

.... with its tasty .... and brightly

.... flowers. The .... sticks to the bee and is

.... with it to the next .... when it flies on.

POLLEN   BEE   NECTAR   FLOWER   COLOURED   CARRIED   STAMEN

Where do flowers vote? — At a pollen station...

Pollen is really important for plant reproduction, but the tricky bit is getting it from one plant to another plant of the same kind — that's where insects are useful. Busy bees have loads of work.

KS2 Science Answers — Life Cycles

Insect pollinated plants have big bright **flowers** to attract insects. Plants pollinated by the **wind** don't need such colourful and eye-catching flowers.

Q2: INSECT   WIND   INSECT   WIND   INSECT

Q3: The top "wind pollinated plants have less chance of their pollen getting to another plant..." box should be ticked.

Page 14 Flower Structure

Q1: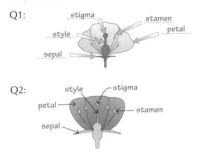
stigma, stamen, style, petal, sepal

Q2: style, stigma, petal, stamen, sepal

Q3 Petals, outside and pollen should all be circled.

Page 15 Different Parts of a Flower

Q1:

FLOWER PART	WHAT IT LOOKS LIKE	WHAT IT DOES
petal	colourful part of the flower	it's bright and scented to attract insects
stamen	long things sticking out from the flower, holding the pollen	to stick pollen onto the insect or release it into the wind
stigma	sticky bit at the top of the long thing sticking straight up on the middle of the flower	catches pollen from insects or the wind
style	stalk-like thing sticking straight up in the middle of the flower	holds the stigma up — pollen goes through it to the ovaries
sepal	green leafy bit underneath the petals	protects the petals while the flower is still growing

Page 16 Pollination and Fertilisation

Q1: 1) Fertilisation
2) Pollination

Q2: 1) Stamen and stigma should be circled.
2) Pollen and ovary should be circled.

Page 17 Plant Processes

Q1:

Page 18 Life Cycle of a Flowering Plant

Q1: 1) Pollination   2) Fertilisation
3) Seed production   4) Seed dispersal
5) Germination

Q2: a) Wind dispersal   b) Animal dispersal

Page 19 Life Cycle of a Flowering Plant

Q1: 1) This is **pollen dispersal**.   2) This is **seed dispersal**.

Q2: a) Possible answers: Wind pollination
b) Possible answers: Animal dispersal; Wind dispersal; Water dispersal; Exploding seeds out of plant.

Q3: Plants disperse **tiny** grains of **pollen** to fertilise other plants of the same type and produce **seeds**. Seeds come in all different shapes and **sizes**, some are even surrounded in heavy **fruit**. Plants also disperse their seeds to spread them over a **wide area** and make sure there are lots more plants like them.

Page 20 Human Growth

Q1:

	Stage of Growth	Age in Years
Ⓐ	babyhood	0-2
Ⓑ	childhood	3-12
Ⓒ	adolescence	13-16
Ⓓ	adulthood	17 +

Q2: The gaps should show the names of people known by the person doing the question.

Q3: wears a nappy — **A**   goes to junior school — **B**
is not growing any more — **D**   can't walk yet — **A**
learns to read and write — **B**   goes to secondary school — **C**
body starts changing at puberty — **C** joints gradually get stiffer — **D**

Page 21 Human and Animal Development

Q1: a) Human   b) Elephant
c) Sheep, elephant, horse   d) Dog
e) Human

Page 22 The Tale of the Orange Roughy

Q1: The Orange Roughy
Q2: The south coast of Australia
Q3: A depth of 1600 m.

Page 23 The Tale of the Orange Roughy

Q4: The "Orange Roughy have very few bones" and the "Orange Roughy keep very well in the freezer" boxes should be ticked.

Q5: a) The number 30 should be ringed.
b) The number 150 should be ringed.

Q6: The fishing nets catch fish of any **age**. If most of the **older** fish are caught before the **breeding** season, there won't be many new fish that year. A lot of the **younger** fish are caught before they're old enough to **reproduce**.

Q7: The dodo is a bird that is now extinct. It was hunted to extinction because it was **easy to catch** and **tasted nice**. If the **Orange Roughy** continues to be **heavily fished**, like it has been over the last 20 years, it could also become **extinct**.

Q8: The "Put limits on the number of fish the fishermen are allowed to catch" and the "ban fishing in some areas" boxes should be ticked.

Page 24 Revision Questions

Q1: gooseberry bush   sunflower   dandelion

Q2: Plants produce **flowers** that turn into **fruit** which contain **seeds**. The fruit gets **eaten** or falls to the ground where the **seeds** grow into new plants.

Q3: animals   wind   water

Q4: Exploding seeds out from plants.

Q5: Temperature **does** affect whether or not a seed germinates.
Light **doesn't** affect whether or not a seed germinates.
Soil **doesn't** affect whether or not a seed germinates.
Water **does** affect whether or not a seed germinates.

Page 25 Revision Questions

Q6: 1) The bee is attracted to the colour and smell of the **petals**.
2) The bee goes into the flower to eat the **nectar**. Pollen from the flower's **stamen** sticks to the bee's **back** and **legs**.
3) The bee flies off in search of more **nectar**.
4) When the bee goes to another flower, some of the **pollen** from the first flower rubs off. We call the whole process **pollination**.

Q7:
stigma, stamen, style, petal, sepal

Q8: Fertilisation

Q9: When seeds start to grow

Q10: babyhood   childhood   adolescence   adulthood

Q11: If no Orange Roughy reproduce then they will become extinct. Any answer that says the same as the above one is fine. Eg If the Orange Roughy aren't allowed to reproduce they will become extinct.

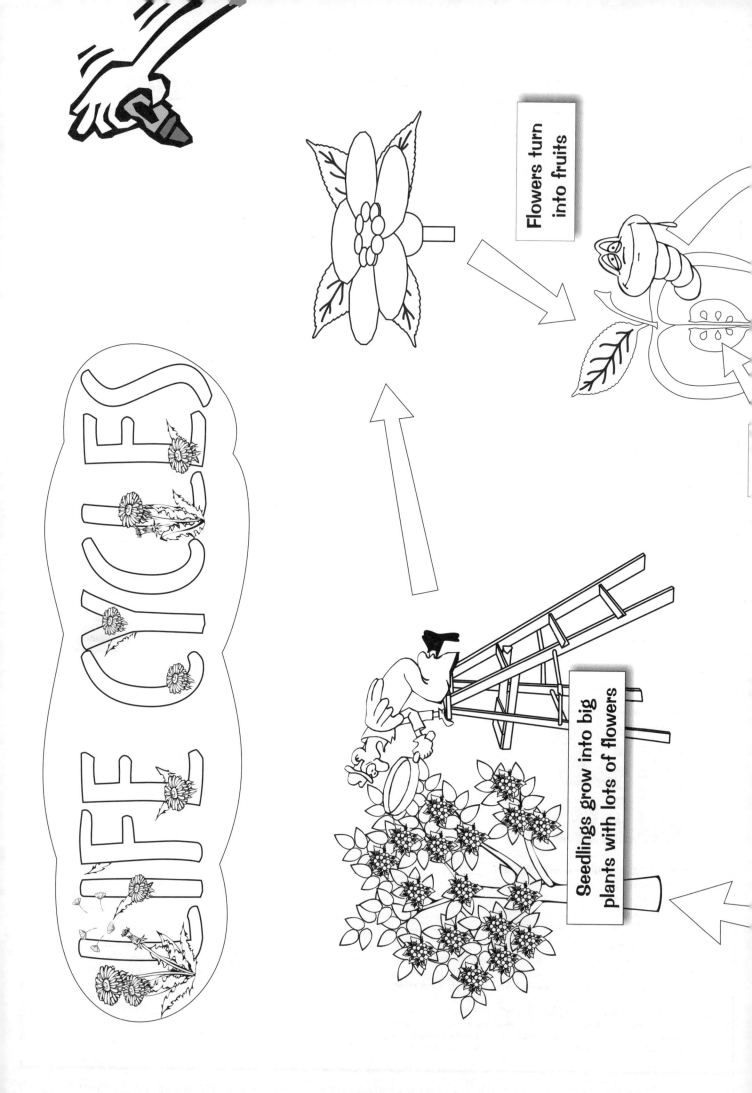

LIFE CYCLES

Flowers turn into fruits

Seedlings grow into big plants with lots of flowers

('pips')

The fruits are eaten by animals

The seeds of the fruit pass through the animal and end up in the ground

GRASS

TOILET

The seeds in the ground grow into new plants

From the CGP KS2 Science book — Life Cycles

KS2 Science Answers — Life Cycles

Page 1 Flowering Plants

Q1: apple tree
pear tree   gooseberry bush
sunflower   dandelion

Q2:

Q3: Plum, orange and lemon should be circled.

Page 2 Flowering Plants

Q1: The fruit grows out of the **flower**.

Q2: The first picture should show a plant with leaves but no flowers. The second picture should show a plant bearing strawberries where the flowers were.

Q3: **Plants** produce **flowers** that turn into **fruit** which contain **seeds**. The fruit gets eaten or **falls** to the ground where the **seeds** grow into new plants.

Page 3 Flowering Plants

Q1: Fruit and seeds are **important** because they fall to the ground and **grow into** new baby plants. Without them there would be **no new** flowering plants.

Q2: Flowering plants reproduce — **Plants with flowers make seeds which grow into new baby plants.**

Q3: All plants grow fruit — **F**
New plants explode out of the middle of flowers — **F**
Flowering plants produce seeds from their flowers — **T**
Fruit grows on the plant where the flowers were, as soon as the flowers fall off — **F**

Page 4 Seed Dispersal and Fruits

Q1:

ANIMAL DISPERSED SEEDS:	WIND DISPERSED SEEDS:
They are surrounded by tasty fruit.	They are not nice to eat.
They are too heavy to float on the wind.	They float easily on the wind.
They are often brightly coloured.	They are very light.

Q2: Cherry — **A**   Sycamore — **W**
Plum — **A**   Thistle — **W**

Q3: A coconut is too **big** to be eaten, too **heavy** to be carried by the wind. Because of this the coconut must be dispersed by **water**.

Page 5 Seed Dispersal and Fruits

Q1: Propeller shaped seed: dispersed by wind, because it is light and streamlined.
Fleshy fruit seed: dispersed by animals because the fruit is tasty and the seeds are too heavy to be dispersed by wind.

Q2: The "to spread their seeds over a wider area" box should be ticked.

Q3: Possible answers:
wind   water   exploding seeds out of plant

Page 6 Germination of Seeds — Warmth

Q1: The "Seeds from some plants grow more quickly than seeds from other plants..." box should be ticked.

Q2: So that the plants can be compared fairly;
So that amount of sunlight doesn't affect results.

Q3: So that the seeds don't get different amounts of sunlight or air;
So that the seeds aren't at different temperatures in the same box.

Page 7 Germination of Seeds — Warmth

Q1:

	2°C	25°C	65°C
2 days	0	0	0
4 days	0	0	0
6 days	0	4	0
8 days	0	9	0
10 days	0	9	0

Q2: Temperature **does** affect whether or not a seed germinates.

Q3: The "25°C" box should be ticked.

Q4: One of the seeds was probably a dead seed.

Page 8 Germination of Seeds — Light

Q1: The three good ways are:
Give all the seeds the same amount of water;
Plant all seeds 1 cm under the soil;
Put half of the pots with seeds in a dark place, and half in a light place.

Q2:

After:	Dark	Light
2 days	0	0
4 days	1	0
6 days	5	4
8 days	8	9
10 days	9	9

Q3: Light **does not** affect whether or not a seed germinates.

Page 9 Germination of Seeds — Soil

Q1: "Give all the seeds the same amount of water" should be ticked.
"Put 10 seeds on kitchen towel, and 10 in soil in a pot" should be ticked.
"Check all the seeds at 9am every other day" should be ticked.
"Make sure all the seeds have the same amount of warmth" should be ticked.

Q2: This table should show the results found by the person who did the experiment. The numbers shown here are from the spare results.

	Number of seeds which had germinated, after...						
	2 days	4 days	6 days	8 days	10 days	12 days	14 days
In soil	0	0	0	0	2	8	9
On kitchen towel	0	0	0	0	3	7	10

Q3: Soil **does not** affect whether or not a seed germinates.

Page 10 Germination of Seeds — Water

Q1:

Bad Way	Good Way
Use seeds from one plant for the seeds with water, and different seeds for the seeds without water.	Uses seeds all from the same plant.
Keep the seeds with water cold, and the seeds without water warm.	Keep all of the seeds the same temperature.
Bury the seeds with water deep in the soil, and the seeds without water just under the surface.	Bury all the seeds at the same depth.

Q2: This table should show the results found by the person who did the experiment. The numbers shown here are from the spare results.

	Number of seeds which had germinated, after...						
	2 days	4 days	6 days	8 days	10 days	12 days	14 days
With water	0	0	0	0	2	8	9
Without water	0	0	0	0	0	0	0

Q3: Water **does** affect whether or not a seed germinates.

Page 11 Germination of Seeds

Q1: This table should show the results found by the person who did the experiment. The numbers shown here are from the spare results.

	Seeds at 2°C	Seeds at 25°C	Seeds at 65°C	Seeds in dark	Seeds in light	Seeds with soil	Seeds without soil	Seeds with water	Seeds without water
Number of seeds that had germinated at the end of the experiment	0	9	0	9	9	9	10	9	0

Q2: Seeds **do** need **water** and the right **temperature** to germinate, but they **don't** need **light** or **soil**.

Q3: Light **does** affect the growth of a plant after germination.
Soil **is** needed by the plant for stability, after germination.

Q4: The best conditions for a seed to germinate and grow into a healthy plant are: 25°C temperature with plenty of water, and in soil with a good light source so that the plant grows well after germination.

Page 12 Insect and Wind Pollination

Q1:

Why does the bee go to the flower?	Bees carry it.
What part of the flower does the pollen come from?	The stamen.
How does the pollen get carried from one plant to the next?	To eat the nectar.
How do plants attract bees?	It sticks to their backs and legs.
How do the bees carry the pollen?	They have brightly coloured flowers.

Q2: The plant makes pollen on its **stamen** inside its flowers. It attracts the **bee** with its tasty **nectar** and brightly **coloured** flowers. The **pollen** sticks to the bee and is **carried** with it to the next **flower** when it flies on.

Page 13 Insect and Wind Pollination

Q1: There are two main types of pollination. **Insect** pollination is where insects like **bees** and beetles **fly** from flower to flower, carrying the sticky pollen with them. The other kind of pollination is **wind** pollination, where the pollen is carried on the wind from one flower to the next.

Insect and Wind Pollination

Some plants _don't_ use insects to help them pollinate, they use the <u>wind</u> instead.
Plants that use wind usually pollinate <u>earlier</u> in the year than the ones which use insects.

Q1   Fill in the gaps using the words in the flowers below. Use each word just once.

There are two main types of pollination. .... pollination is where insects like

.... and beetles .... from flower to flower, carrying the

sticky pollen with them. The other kind of pollination is ....

pollination, where the pollen is carried on the wind from one flower to the next.

.... pollinated plants have big bright ....

to attract insects. Plants pollinated by the .... don't need

such colourful and eye-catching flowers.

WIND   BEES   FLY   WIND   FLOWERS   INSECT   INSECT

Q2   Look at these pictures of flowers and write 'WIND' next to the wind
pollinated ones and 'INSECT' next to the insect pollinated ones.

....
....

Q3   Wind pollinated plants produce more pollen than insect pollinated ones.
Why do think this might be? Tick the right answer from this list of reasons.

Wind pollinated plants have less chance of their pollen getting to another plant
of the same kind — so they need to produce more pollen to make up for it.   ☐

Wind pollinated plants try to spread their pollen to turn the skies yellow.   ☐

The pollen from wind pollinated plants is smaller, so they need to
produce lots to have the same amount as insect pollinated plants.   ☐

Aaa—tchoo!
I'll never be
a gardener now.

Hay fever made
Natasha change
her plans.

Q4   People who get hay fever are allergic to pollen. A high pollen count
means there's a lot of pollen in the air, and people with hay fever suffer
more. Do you think insect pollinated or wind pollinated plants cause
the biggest problem for hay fever sufferers?   ....
....

English nation, French nation & pollination...

All flowering plants need to get their pollen to another flower — some use insects to help them and
others use the wind. And pollen in the air is bad news for people with hay fever. At-chooooooooo.

Flower Structure

Just as animals have to produce more animals, flowers have to find a way of producing more flowers.

Q14 Fill in the labels on this flower — choose from the words in the box.

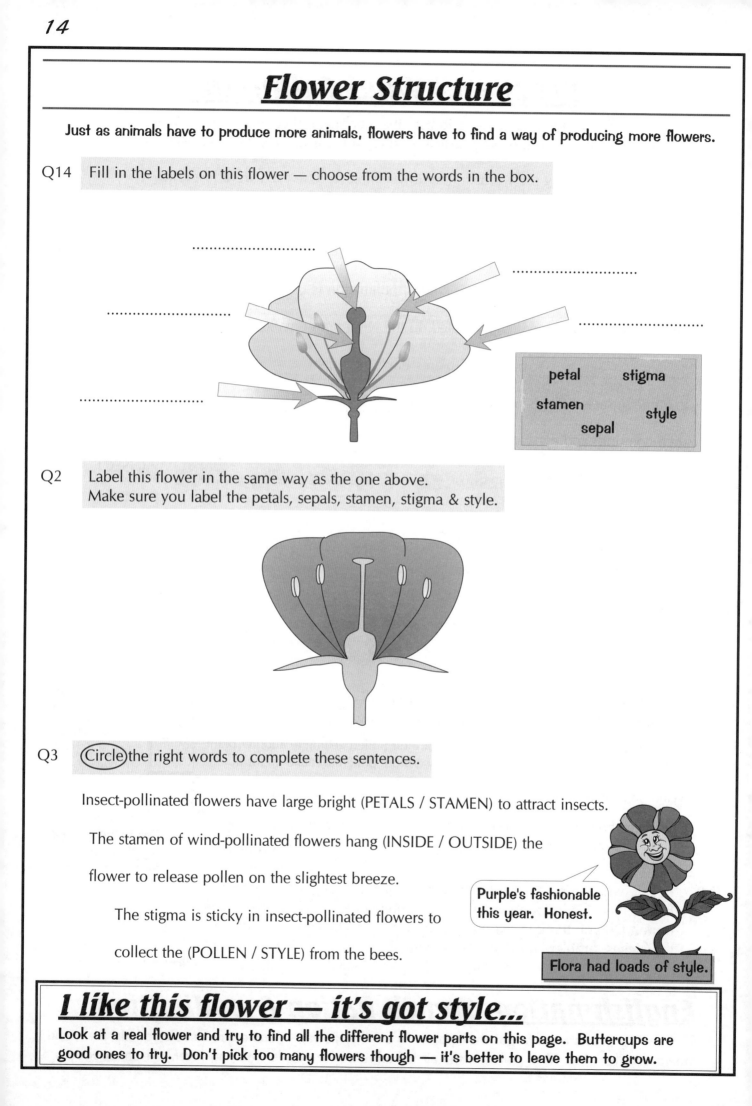

petal   stigma
stamen
style
sepal

Q2 Label this flower in the same way as the one above.
Make sure you label the petals, sepals, stamen, stigma & style.

Q3 Circle the right words to complete these sentences.

Insect-pollinated flowers have large bright (PETALS / STAMEN) to attract insects.

The stamen of wind-pollinated flowers hang (INSIDE / OUTSIDE) the

flower to release pollen on the slightest breeze.

The stigma is sticky in insect-pollinated flowers to

collect the (POLLEN / STYLE) from the bees.

Purple's fashionable this year. Honest.

Flora had loads of style.

I like this flower — it's got style...

Look at a real flower and try to find all the different flower parts on this page. Buttercups are good ones to try. Don't pick too many flowers though — it's better to leave them to grow.

Different Parts of a Flower

Flowers have quite a few parts to them, mostly with strange names — although 'petal' is fairly normal. If you can fill in this table, you'll be a flower expert in no time.

Q1 This table shows what different parts of a flower look like and what they're there for. Some of it's missing — fill in the gaps from the words underneath the table.

FLOWER PART	WHAT IT LOOKS LIKE	WHAT IT DOES
	colourful part of the flower	
	long things sticking out from the flower, holding the pollen	
		catches pollen from insects or the wind
style		
sepal		

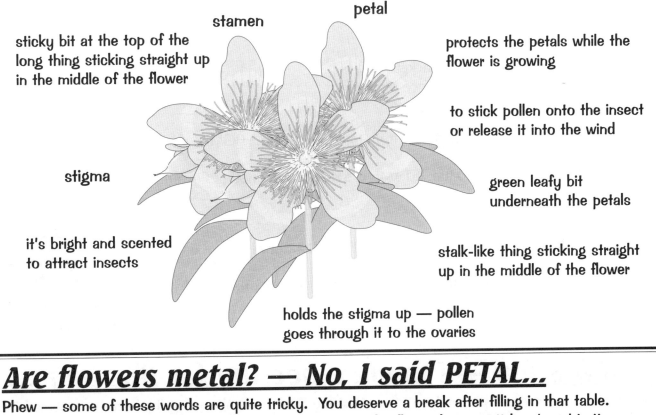

stamen   petal

sticky bit at the top of the long thing sticking straight up in the middle of the flower

protects the petals while the flower is growing

to stick pollen onto the insect or release it into the wind

stigma

green leafy bit underneath the petals

it's bright and scented to attract insects

stalk-like thing sticking straight up in the middle of the flower

holds the stigma up — pollen goes through it to the ovaries

Are flowers metal? — No, I said PETAL...

Phew — some of these words are quite tricky. You deserve a break after filling in that table. A quick hint — remember that sta__men__ is the male part of a flower because it has '__men__' in it.

16

Pollination and Fertilisation

Take a deep breath — <u>pollination</u> and <u>fertilisation</u> are not the same, and you have to know the difference between them. Pollination comes first.

Q1 One of these diagrams shows pollination, the other shows fertilisation. The black arrows show the direction the pollen is going in each one. Label each diagram '<u>pollination</u>' or '<u>fertilisation</u>'.

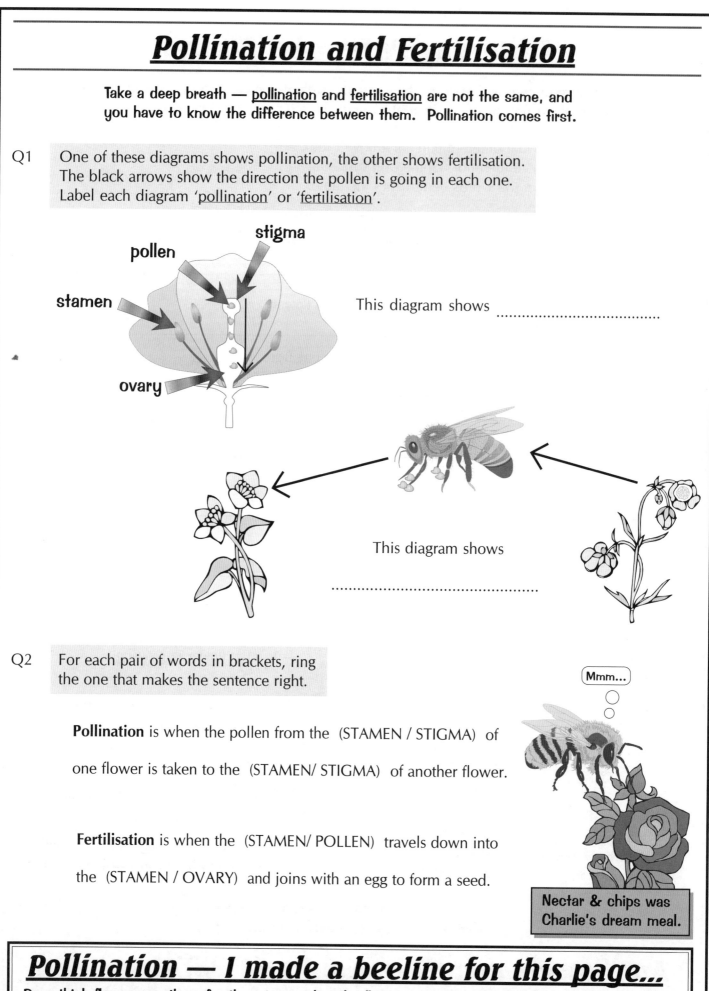

This diagram shows ....

This diagram shows ....

Q2 For each pair of words in brackets, ring the one that makes the sentence right.

Mmm...

Pollination is when the pollen from the (STAMEN / STIGMA) of one flower is taken to the (STAMEN / STIGMA) of another flower.

Fertilisation is when the (STAMEN / POLLEN) travels down into the (STAMEN / OVARY) and joins with an egg to form a seed.

Nectar & chips was Charlie's dream meal.

Pollination — I made a beeline for this page...

Bees think flowers are there for them to use, but the flowers are also using the bees — to spread their pollen, so that it can be fertilised and new flowers will grow. So both the bees and flowers are happy.

Plant Processes

Plants aren't just there to give us something pretty to look at. They have clever ways of making sure that, when they die, there'll be other plants in their place.

Q1   This crossword is all about how plants reproduce. Go for it.

ACROSS

1) Posh name for the seeds being scattered.

4) What happens when the pollen meets an egg.

5) Insect that carries pollen from one plant to another.

7) Leafy thing that protects the petals when the flower is still a bud.

9) The top part of the female reproductive organs — it's sticky to catch pollen.

10) Part of the female reproductive organs — the place the pollen has to go in order to fertilise the egg.

DOWN

2) Posh word for when the pollen from one flower reaches another flower.

3) The male part of a flower — the bit containing the pollen.

4) It contains seeds and is sometimes tasty.

6) Colourful part of a flower.

8) Something that carries the pollen if an insect doesn't.

9) The middle part of the female organs of the flower — it holds up the stigma.

But flowers can't dance!

Buzz didn't think much of Betsy's new dancing partner.

Flower crossword — flowers never give me a cross word...

Tremendous. If you've finished the crossword without looking anything up, well done! If you do get a bit stuck, don't worry, just look back at the last three pages for more clues.

Life Cycle of a Flowering Plant

You already know loads of stuff about how plants reproduce. This page goes over all that stuff again to make sure you can really remember it. You need to know what order things happen in.

Q1 These pictures show the life cycle of a poppy. Use the words from the box on the right to fill in the name of each stage on the dotted lines.

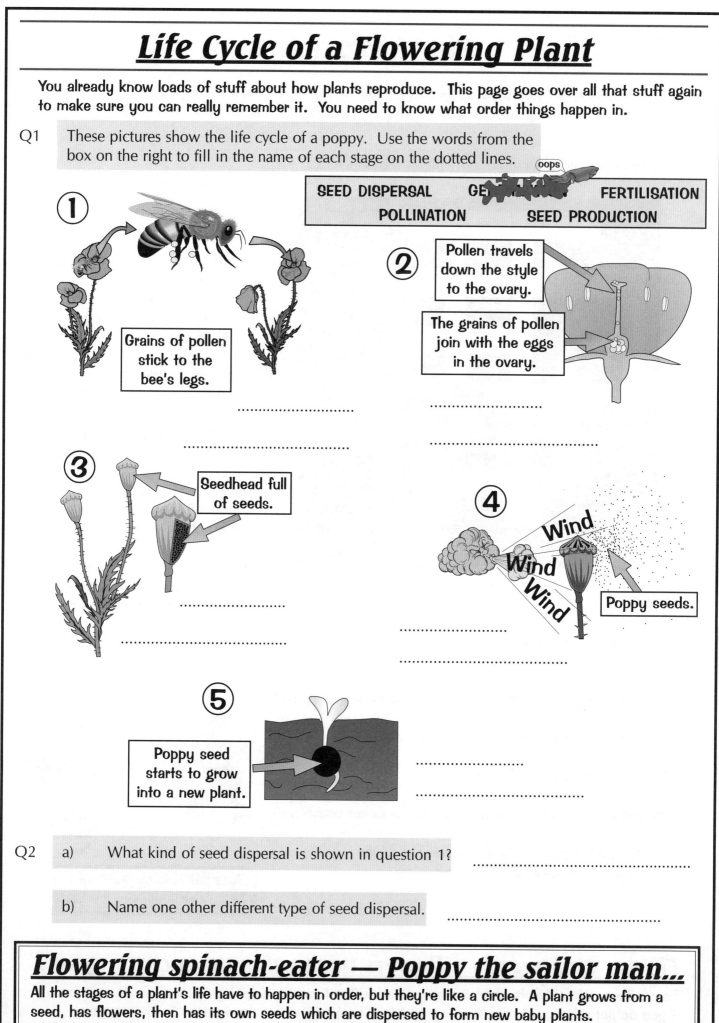

oops

SEED DISPERSAL   GE~~~~~~~~~~~   FERTILISATION
POLLINATION   SEED PRODUCTION

① Grains of pollen stick to the bee's legs.

....

....

② Pollen travels down the style to the ovary.

The grains of pollen join with the eggs in the ovary.

....

....

③ Seedhead full of seeds.

....

....

④ Wind Wind Wind   Poppy seeds.

....

....

⑤ Poppy seed starts to grow into a new plant.

....

....

Q2 a) What kind of seed dispersal is shown in question 1?

....

b) Name one other different type of seed dispersal.

....

Flowering spinach-eater — Poppy the sailor man...

All the stages of a plant's life have to happen in order, but they're like a circle. A plant grows from a seed, has flowers, then has its own seeds which are dispersed to form new baby plants.

Life Cycle of a Flowering Plant

You've already done stuff about pollen and seed dispersal so this
should be a breeze. Do this page to make sure you've got it.

Q1 Here are descriptions of two different kinds of dispersal.
Write 'seed dispersal' next to one, and 'pollination' next to the other.

Small grains are dispersed from the flower of the plant. These grains need to find their
way to another flower of the same kind and join with the plant's eggs in the ovary.

This is ....

Larger grains are dispersed by the plant. They spread over a wide
area and try to find a patch of ground to germinate and grow in.

This is ....

Q2 a) Name a type of pollination different from the one above and draw a picture of it.
b) Name a type of seed dispersal different from the one above and draw a picture of it.

POLLINATION:

....

SEED DISPERSAL:

....

HALF TIME ORANGES

Lewis was very glad
some seeds come
wrapped in fruit.

Q3 Fill in the gaps using the words from the box.

Plants disperse .... grains of .... to fertilise

other plants of the same type so they can make .... Seeds come

in all different shapes and ...., some are even surrounded in

heavy .... Plants also disperse their seeds to spread them over a

.... and make sure there are lots more plants like them.

SIZES
TINY
WIDE AREA
FRUIT
POLLEN
SEEDS

Pollen and seed dispersal — sneezy peasy...

Plants need pollen to fertilise their eggs which then become seeds. Then they disperse their seeds,
scattering them far away to give their new baby plants plenty of room to grow into big plants.

20

Human Growth

There are different <u>stages of growth</u> between being born and becoming 'grown-up'.
When a <u>baby</u> is born, it's helpless, but an <u>adult</u> is able to look after him or herself.

This is Sally in different stages of her life.

Ⓐ   Ⓑ   Ⓒ   Ⓓ

Q1   Fill in the table about these stages of growth.
The words and ages are in the blob below.

childhood   13 - 16
adulthood
0 - 2   17 +   babyhood
adolescence   3 - 12

	Stage of Growth	Age in Years
Ⓐ		
Ⓑ		
Ⓒ		
Ⓓ		

Q2   a)   Write the name of the stage of human growth you are at.   ....

b)   Try to think of two people who are at two of the other three
stages. Write down their names and the stage they are at.

.... is at the .... stage.

.... is at the .... stage.

Q3   Put a letter (A-D) next to each of these sentences,
to show which stage of growth they're talking about.

wears a nappy ....   goes to junior school ....   is not growing any more ....

can't walk yet ....   learns to read and write ....   goes to secondary school ....

body starts changing at puberty ....   joints gradually get stiffer ....

Life — you'll grow into it...

It takes humans ages to become adult and able to look after themselves completely — about 16
years. Most of the stages are easy to understand — it's not hard to work out what babyhood is.

Human and Animal Development

Not all animals take as <u>long</u> as humans to grow up and be able to look after <u>themselves</u>. In fact, it takes most animals much <u>less</u> time than humans.

Q1 This table compares the development of some animals, including humans. Look at it carefully and answer the questions below.

Animal	How long the mother carries it before it's born	Age when it can eat solid food	Age when it can walk	Age when it becomes adult	How long it lives
Human	9 months	1 year	14 months	16 years	80 years
Sheep	5 months	4 months	Immediately	1 year	13 years
Elephant	20-21 months	2 years	Immediately	25 years	60 years
Horse	11 months	6 months	Immediately	5 years	20-25 years
Dog	63 days	4 weeks	10-14 days	2 years	12 years

a) Which animal lives the longest?

   ....

b) Which animal is carried by the mother for the longest time before it is born?

   ....

c) Which animals start to walk as soon as they have been born?

   ....

d) Which animal learns to eat at the youngest age?

   ....

e) Which animal takes longest to learn to walk?

   ....

Learning how to use his trunk was a big step forward for Egbert.

Childhood — longer than most other hoods...

Humans take a lot longer to grow up than most young animals — but then humans live longer as well. Remember that the lengths of time in the table aren't always exactly right — some people live longer than others, and not every mother dog will have her puppies in exactly 63 days.

The Tale of the Orange Roughy

Meet the <u>Orange Roughy</u>. The Orange Roughy is a kind of <u>fish</u> that is dying out because of the fishing industry. But there's more to it than that — the Orange Roughy has a <u>different life cycle</u> from most fish — read on and find out more...

CASE STUDY

Save the Orange Roughy

The deep sea waters off the South Coast of Australia are home to a remarkable fish called the Orange Roughy. This amazing fish can live as long as 150 years, and lives at a depth of 1600 m — that's more than five Eiffel Towers deep!

Unfortunately for the Orange Roughy, it has become very popular on dinner tables in America. That's because it's got hardly any bones in it, which makes it dead easy to scoff quickly. The fish are also perfect for freezing — and that's really important for supermarkets and restaurants, because they're easier to store.

The big problem is that the Roughy doesn't start to reproduce until it's 30 years old. If all these older fish are caught in one year, no new fish will be born — and none of the remaining Roughies will reach breeding age for a long time.

Twenty years ago there were no limits on how many fish could be caught, so the Orange Roughy were mercilessly over-fished. Thousands of tonnes of them were trawled up from the breeding grounds — and as you might guess, this has dramatically reduced its numbers.

Q1   What's the name of the fish that's being talked about?

....

Q2   In what part of the world is the fish found?

....

Q3   How deep down in the ocean does it live?

....

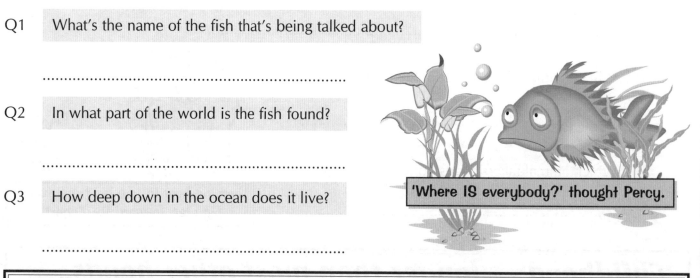

'Where IS everybody?' thought Percy.

The Orange Roughy — it gets a bit of a rough deal...

Scary stuff. People like <u>eating</u> Orange Roughy, but if we keep fishing <u>too many</u> of them, they'll end up <u>dying out</u>. And then there'd be <u>no more</u> Orange Roughy at all. Save the Orange Roughy!

The Tale of the Orange Roughy

Q4   Why does the fishing industry like the Orange Roughy? Tick the two right answers.

People like the colour of the fish ☐   Orange Roughy keep very well in the freezer ☐

Orange Roughy have very few bones ☐   The Orange Roughy give the
                                               fishermen walnut cake ☐

Q5   Read each sentence carefully and ring the right answer.

   a)   Orange Roughy can't reproduce until they are (3 / 30 / 150) years old.

   b)   Orange Roughy can live for up to (30 / 150 / 300) years.

Q6   Fill in the blanks in this paragraph about the Orange Roughy.

   The fishing nets catch fish of any .... If most of the .... fish are

   caught before the .... season, there won't be many new fish that year. A lot

   of the .... fish are caught before they're old enough to ....

   (reproduce)   (younger)   (age)   (breeding)   (older)

Q7   Use the words in the bubbles to complete the
      paragraph about how animals become extinct.

      heavily fished
      tasted nice   extinct
      Orange Roughy
      easy to catch

   The dodo is a bird that is now extinct. It was hunted to extinction

   because it was .... and ....

   If the .... continues to be ...., like it has

   been over the last 20 years, it could also become ....

Q8   How could we stop the Orange Roughy from becoming extinct?
      Put a tick next to the suggestions you think would work.

                     Put limits on the number of fish the fishermen are allowed to catch ☐

Leave things the way they are ☐   Ban fishing in some areas ☐

           Think up tasty new recipes for the Orange Roughy ☐

Dinosaurs had smelly eggs — eggs-stinkt...

The Orange Roughy is now an 'endangered species'. That means it's in danger of becoming extinct.
But it's not just the Roughy — the Panda, the Tiger and the Cheetah are also endangered species.

Revision Questions

Zikes! It's 'see-how-many-questions-we-can-squeeze-on-a-page' time. Here are two pages squashed full of questions that ask you about stuff you've already done in this book — go get 'em.

Q1 Look at the fruits and flowers below and write the name of the plant they came from underneath them. Choose plant names from the box.

Apple Tree
Dandelion
Gooseberry bush
Sunflower
Tulip

....

Q2 Fill in the gaps in these sentences using one of the choices from the brackets.

Plants produce .... (FLOWERS/SEEDS) that turn into .... (LEAVES/FRUIT)

which contain .... (FLOWERS/SEEDS). The fruit gets .... (LIGHTER/

EATEN) or falls to the ground where the .... (FRUIT/SEEDS) grow into new plants.

Q3 Write after the following seeds how they are dispersed.
Choose from the following: by the wind, by animals, by water.

Cherry   Sycamore   Coconut

....

Q4 Name one type of seed dispersal that isn't mentioned above. ....

Q5 Draw a ring around the right word in the brackets to complete these sentences.

Temperature [DOES / DOESN'T] affect whether or not a seed germinates.

Light [DOES / DOESN'T] affect whether or not a seed germinates.

Soil [DOES / DOESN'T] affect whether or not a seed germinates.

Water [DOES / DOESN'T] affect whether or not a seed germinates.

Look over there to play page ping pong → → →

"Science is full of questions, of which these are just a few,
answer these lovely questions, and do the next page too." I'll think I'll leave poetry to the experts...

Revision Questions

Q6   Fill in the words below to describe how a bee pollinates a flower.

a) The bee is attracted to the colour and smell of the ....

b) The bee goes into the flower to eat the .... Pollen from the flower's

.... sticks to the bee's .... and ....

c) The bee flies off in search of more ....

d) When the bee goes to another flower, some of the .... from the first flower

rubs off. We call the whole process ....

Q7   Fill in the labels on this flower — choose from the words in the box.

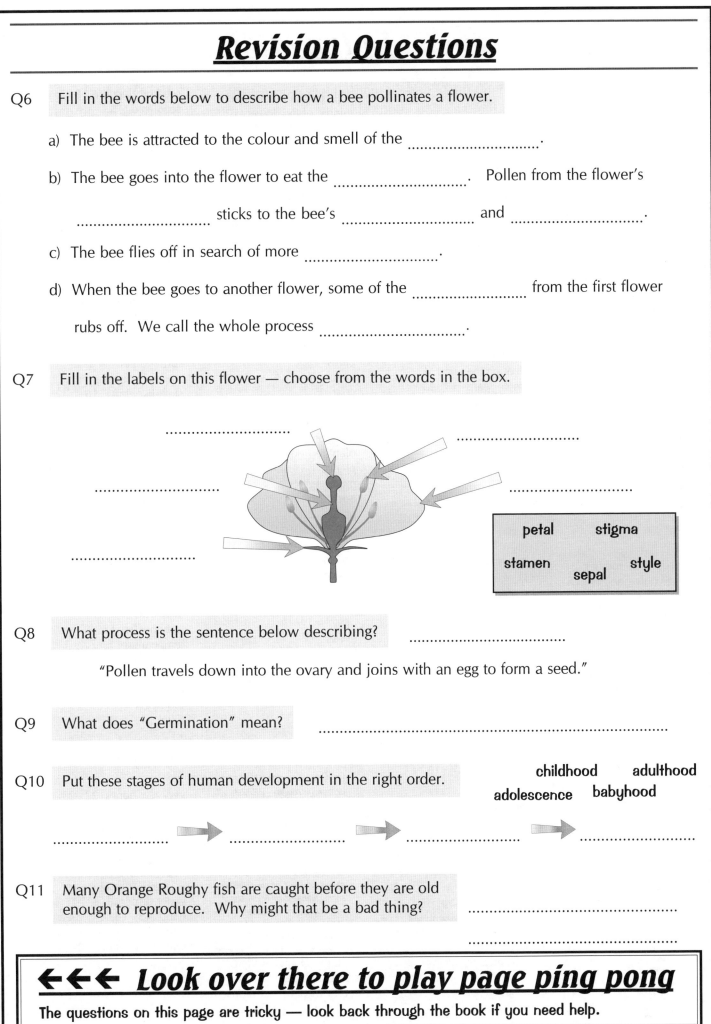

....

....

....

....

petal	stigma
stamen	style
sepal	

Q8   What process is the sentence below describing?   ....

"Pollen travels down into the ovary and joins with an egg to form a seed."

Q9   What does "Germination" mean?   ....

Q10   Put these stages of human development in the right order.   childhood   adulthood
adolescence   babyhood

.... → .... → .... → ....

Q11   Many Orange Roughy fish are caught before they are old
enough to reproduce. Why might that be a bad thing?   ....

....

←←← Look over there to play page ping pong

The questions on this page are tricky — look back through the book if you need help.

Index